Testimonials

Adoption is a magical, heartfelt full-circle blessing. I was chosen when my birth mother was unable to provide the necessary care. In my loving and accepting family, I never knew I was different from any other sibling or cousin or even schoolmates. It was not until years later when the value of this gift was appreciated...

One's blessings are to be shared and passed along. So, more than thirty years ago, I adopted two young boys, and along the way, we adopted several young and middle-aged dogs to round out our family. We are simply blessed!

—D.A. Yocham

When a parent longs for a child, and a child longs for a parent, those desires meet in a beautiful gift called adoption and create an even more beautiful thing—a family.

—Valeria B., adoption attorney

Adoption allows children to find forever homes with parents choosing to love them loudly and proudly each and every day. Children get to be loved in a meaningful and intentional way that caters to healing and nurturing their growth and development.

—K.B., social worker

Adoption is one of the sweetest pictures of God's love for us as He has adopted us into His family and called us His own children. To feel chosen, loved, celebrated, and home is something that every child longs for, and adoption is such an incredible story of that longing being met.

—Macy D., child advocate

Adoption is to be given a gift you could never earn or deserve. It is the building of a family through love, sacrifice, vulnerability, and faith. Simply put, adoption is a gift of grace upon grace.

—L. Schank, adoptive family

I love being Sumo's pet sitter and a member of his extended family. Sumo's health and safety are big responsibilities and when his parents are away, I care for Sumo as if he were my dog.

—Trish G., Peace of Mind Pet Services

We love taking care of all of the special animals in our community. Sometimes, certain pets stand out just a little more than others. They have that special something about them—that extra sparkle in their eye. That was Sumo. Each time he visited, he walked in the door so proudly. He would put his paws up on the counter, just to say, "Hi! I'm here! Please come pet me, now." He always had a way of making us all smile.

—Fred S. Baron, DVM

Finding My Forever Family

by SUMO

ISBN: 978-1-64184-370-6 (paperback)
ISBN: 978-1-64184-380-5 (hardback)

Contents

Sumo's Dedication ix

Introduction xi

Traveling to Texas 1

Meeting My New Sister 6

My Second Day in Texas 10

Rules of the House 14

My Special Name 18

Sumo Goes to the Doctor 20

Sumo Gets New Teeth! 22

Something Called Work 26

Sumo Goes to School 27

Sumo Practices Doga 31

Sumo Goes for Rides 37

Sumo Loves the Backyard   40

Sumo Goes to the Groomer   44

Sometimes Parents Need a Vacation   48

Sumo Goes to the Country   54

Sumo Goes to the Farmers' Market   58

Sumo Moves to the Country   63

Sumo's Forever Family   66

Sumo Meets His New Neighbor   68

Afterward   71

Sumo's Dedication

To Dad, who allowed Mom to bring another special family member into their lives. Little did Dad know how important I would be in his life and how the unconditional love we shared would carry us through some rough days ahead. Thank you, Dad, for caring for me, for the attention, and for the special meals you prepared for me. We are all grateful.

Introduction

The purpose of this book is to share a simple story of adoption from a dog's point of view. It is for all the children in the world who have found their forever homes and for the parents and families who opened their hearts and homes. For all the emotions and sacrifices you will experience along the way, it is worth it!

Traveling to Texas

It was a cool fall day on a farm in Lexington, Kentucky, where a small 8-week-old black and white Akita puppy named White Socks was running and playing in a fenced yard in the countryside. The owner of the farm picked up White Socks and told him, "I have some very exciting news for you today! A family in Texas wants to adopt you! Today you get to ride on a plane!"

I was feeling a little scared and excited as we headed to the airport. What was a plane? How long would it take? Who were these people? I would miss my sisters and brothers. I didn't know how I felt about it then!

I got to take a car ride to the airport. I found out immediately that I LOVE car rides! I liked looking out the window and seeing new things along the road.

When we got to the airport, they put me into a big box called a "crate" and put my crate on a plane. At first, this was scary because I had never

been in a crate. The crate was belted in tight. Then I saw the crate was to help me be safe. The plane was cold and noisy, but I liked the cool air. I lay down in my safe crate and took a nap. The plane landed in Atlanta, and then they took me to another plane! There were so many people and so much noise! It was very frightening. I was not sure I should have left the farm in Kentucky. What if I got lost? What if I couldn't find my new family? What if they couldn't find me? I was scared! Finally, I got sleepy and took another nap. Wow, it was a long way to Texas! I hoped everything would be OK. I had to trust these new people.

At last I got to Houston Hobby Airport. It was confusing. There were a lot of people there and everybody was rushing by my crate. I wondered which ones would be my new Daddy and Mommy. Was that him? Was that her? A man named Dad picked me up. He had all the official papers to take me home. He was kind and held me. I was so glad to be off the plane! I gave him lots of licks – those are dog kisses!

All of a sudden, several ladies came over to see me. They wanted to pet me. They said I was the cutest puppy they had ever seen! (I WAS a cute puppy!) Dad held me tight. I felt safe. Then Dad took me for a walk and gave me some water. I was so thirsty after that plane ride, and I needed to go potty! Bad! Dad knew just what I needed right then and there.

Dad put me in a big green truck with him, and he started driving. I was not sure where we were going. There were lots of strange sounds

4

that I never heard in the country. There was a fire engine, a police car, a car exhaust, -- so many cars on the road! It was not like this living in the country in Kentucky. It was a little bit scary! But I felt safe with Dad. He was someone I could trust.

The truck stopped and Dad picked me up and gently put me on the ground. He told me we were at a church. We were not home yet. He let me walk around and explore. It was fun. There were big magnolia leaves on the ground that I could push with my nose. There were flowers I could smell. There were pinecones on the ground...yikes! They were prickly!

Meeting My New Sister

Just a few minutes later a lady name Mom and another dog walked by. The other dog was an Akita, like me. She was a girl dog named Miso. Dad said hello to them. They were friendly.

Miso and I walked towards each other, then all around each other and sniffed. Miso was about three years old. She was OK, but she was kind of big! I wondered, "Who is this big dog?" *Miso thought: "Who is this puppy? Why are Mom and Dad here at the church? I think I need to check this puppy out."* She came closer and sniffed and licked me all over. Miso kissed me from the top of my head to my paws! It was almost like I was getting a love bath.

Once we were all together, we started walking down the street. Dad stopped and opened a gate. He told me we were home. There were big front porch steps. I could not climb the steps, so Mom picked me up, snuggled her face in my fur, kissed me, and carried me inside. Dad and Miso followed into the house. *Miso wondered, "How come this puppy is following us into the house? This is my house!"*

Mom put me down on the floor. I had never been on a wood floor before. It was slippery but fun! Mom told me Miso was my new dog sister. I was excited to know I would have a sister and would not be alone. I saw that Miso and I have the same black and white fur, although she has a few brown spots.

Miso walked to the back of the house, and I followed her wherever she went. I began to explore the house. There were all kinds of hiding places like behind the couch and the chairs and the plants. They had plants inside their house!

Miso got tired of me following her everywhere and lay down on the rug by the door. Mom thought that Miso was not sure about me yet, but I wanted to get to know her. Mom sat down on the rug and played with both of us.

Miso was thinking "When is this puppy going to go home? I like being the only Akita."

I thought, "This family seems kind, but what is going on with big Miso? She does not seem happy I am here. I wonder why?" I was glad that Mom was going to be my new mommy and Dad was going to be my new daddy. I hoped this is going to be my forever family, but you never know.

Then it was time for dinner. Mom put two bowls of food and water on the floor for me and two bowls for Miso. Then Dad and Mom sat down at a table for their dinner. They all started eating dinner as a family. I looked at my food, then I smelled it, but I really did not feel hungry.

After dinner we all went to bed. More stairs! Miso ran up fast, but I couldn't walk up by myself. Mom carried me again. We all got to sleep in the same room. I think they knew I needed to be with them even though Miso stayed on Dad's side kind of far away from me. It had been a long day.

My Second Day in Texas

The next day Mom woke me up and kissed me good morning. She took me outside into the yard to go potty. It was a pretty day. She talked to me while I explored. There were some cool plants to hide behind. There was a big rock. There were some pretty flowers. There was a black iron fence around the yard to keep me safe so I couldn't go into the street with dangerous cars.

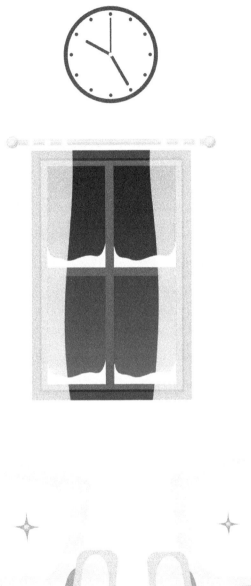

11

Mom explained to me about adoption. She said out of all the puppies, they chose ME! They loved me from my internet photos. (I WAS such a cute puppy!) Mom and Dad had to have many very long interviews and fill out lots of paperwork. (What are "interviews?") They had to prove they could give me a good, safe home. They got a ticket to fly me to Texas when the temperature was not too hot. Mom said they had to file some final paperwork and it would take a few months, but everything would be fine. Houston and this family would be my forever home. I was happy because I knew they chose me and loved me, and I was very lucky to have been adopted by this family.

Mom took me inside and gave me water and food. Mom noticed I was not hungry. I was happy in my new home, but I was a little sad to leave Kentucky. I was not sure why.

Mom felt something was wrong and did not know what. She called the man on the farm in Kentucky and explained I was not eating. He laughed. He said "I forgot to tell you the secret. White Socks loves yogurt." Mom said "Ok. This is good to know, and I will go to the store right now."

She left and I did not know where she was going or why. Dad and Miso were home so Mom left me with them. She was only gone a few minutes. She walked back into the house with a bag. She took out the yogurt and put it on top my food. I knew then she went to the store just for me!

I went to my food bowl and ate all my food. This reminded me of home. Mom was so happy I ate all my food. After breakfast she took me outside again to potty. She took me outside to go potty very often. I know she did that so I would not have an accident in the house. I did not want that, and I know she did not want that. She said I was a good dog!

Rules of the House

Mom talked to me. She explained when you live with a family there are certain rules you must follow. This was new to me because I came from the country and lived outside, and I do not think we had rules. The first rule was to get along with my sister. By now, Miso had warmed up to me, and we were playing and doing things together. We were rewarded when we got along.

The second rule was that every morning and night we must brush our teeth -- whatever that means! Then she took out a special toothbrush and toothpaste just for me. She put toothpaste on the brush with water. She let me smell it. It smelled minty. Next, she put the brush in my mouth and brushed my teeth and gums. It tickled. It was fun. She rinsed off the brush with water and rinsed out my mouth. She told me I was a good boy! I liked the special attention she gave me. So, that was one of the rules I had to learn.

Mom took me to the kitchen. She got a Greenie from the treat can. Greenies are a special treat for me that help my teeth. I love those treats! They are my rewards for being a good boy. This treat thing is cool! So, I guess if I follow the rules, good things happen. Mom said there would be more rules later. If rules have treats, I am all in!

My Special Name

Mom and Dad did not like the name "White Socks," even though it really is the way I look. I have black fur with white on my face and neck, tummy, legs and paws, and the very tip of my tail. They wanted me to have a Japanese name. My grandparents and great-grandparents were from Japan. I thought I was from Kentucky, so who knew? I learned that my dog birth parents were from Kentucky.

Mom and Dad wanted me to be true to my family roots. Mom and Dad believed if we spent a few days together we could think of a better name. They tried a few but nothing stuck. On the third day, we were outside. I was at one end of the driveway, and they were at the other end. All of sudden, they yelled "Sumo!" I stopped immediately and turned to look at them. We all knew that "Sumo" was the perfect new name for me. Sumo means "healthy, to rush at, likes to compete and get plenty of exercise." I had found my new home and a new name just for me.

Sumo Goes to the Doctor

I arrived in Houston on a Friday night. Mom and Dad wanted me to settle into our home before taking me to the doctor for the first time. Then they took me to the veterinarian – that's a dog doctor. Mom and Dad wanted to be sure I was healthy. On Monday morning we got into the car, and we went to the veterinarian to get me checked out. They weighed me, took my temperature, checked my teeth, took some blood, gave me two shots, and took my picture. I really did not like the shots, but I loved getting my picture taken. I WAS a cute puppy, you know!

The veterinarian gave me a treat for being such a good boy. I heard her tell Mom and Dad that I was very healthy and a very special Akita. She told them to take good care of me. The doctor said she would see me in six months for another checkup and more shots. (I do not like shots, but I am brave. And the vet has treats.)

When we got home, I took a nap. Mom called my old home in Kentucky to tell them I was in good health. Now Mom and Dad could finish my adoption. Two months later, the final adoption papers arrived, and I was a legal member of the family. While I was very excited, I think Mom and Dad were even happier, because that night they had a party for me! We had special food and treats and a special doggie cake to celebrate our new family.

Sumo Gets New Teeth!

About a month later when I was twelve weeks old, something strange happened. I was lying on the rug in the front room, and I lost one of my teeth! Mom saw the tooth lying on the floor and picked it up. There was a little blood, and I was freaked out, but it didn't hurt. Mom saved the tooth. She told me all puppies -- and even kids -- lose baby teeth. She told me I was growing up. A few days later, I lost another tooth! Mom saw it on the rug and picked it up. She saved those baby teeth. I was less freaked out the second time. I got an extra treat each time I lost a tooth. She gave me a small bowl of yogurt and ice in my water bowl to help my mouth feel better. Losing teeth was kind of cool because I got an extra treat. I am a good dog.

My teeth all grew back, and the new teeth are much bigger! When all my teeth had grown back in, they gave me a small rawhide bone to chew. Wow, was that exciting! I spent hours chewing and chewing the bone.

Miso had her own bone too. The chew bones helped our teeth. Mom and Dad always made sure to take care of us.

Then one day I chewed and chewed the rawhide bone and broke off one of my big teeth! Nobody noticed for a day or two until Mom and Dad saw I was not eating. I was hurting but I didn't know how to tell them what was wrong. We went back to my doctor. She took pictures called "x-rays" and saw I had broken a tooth. She said I needed to go to a special dog dentist. Mom made the appointment. The dog dentist told us what was going to happen. She would take out the tooth. Mom and Dad did not want the tooth to hurt me, so they told the dentist to take it out. After it was out, Mom and Dad came to pick me up. I was so sleepy, and all I wanted to do was go home and sleep! For the next few days, I could not eat regular dog food. I had to have a special soft canned dog food and rice. It was delicious! Another treat for being a good, brave dog!

Something Called Work

I soon learned that Mom and Dad had jobs. That meant they would leave me and Miso for the day, which I thought was scary. I didn't want to be alone! I soon found out that Mom and Dad would not leave us all alone. Mom has a mom who is my grandmother, and her name is Mere. The cool thing was that she came to the house every day to work for Dad's business. She was the office manager, and the office was in our house. Handy! Now we were with her every day of the week.

Mere was very busy on the phone, but she did not mind if we stayed close by her desk. When Mere took her lunch break, we got to play with her. She loves dogs! She loves us! Our grandmother spoiled us with treats and love. She carried a special stash of treats in her purse to share with us. I do not think she told Mom and Dad about the treats. It was our secret. Now I had a bigger family. I love my big family in Texas!

Sumo Goes to School

Dad and Mom knew I would grow up to be a big boy one day. They wanted to make sure I had good manners. This is another rule of the house. A dog teacher came to the house. We called him my "trainer." I was home schooled. He first let me come up to him. Then he put my leash on me and walked me up and down the driveway. I followed him while he talked to me. Sometimes we would walk straight. Sometimes we would do circle eights. He called me by my name. He watched me. He would tell me things like "sit" and "heel" and "stay." Every time he gave me a command, he showed me what to do. Once he showed me, I did just what he said. He praised me every time I did what he asked. He said I was a good boy. I have a special gift. My trainer taught Mom and Dad how to practice with me every day. We learned together. We are a family.

After learning outside, my trainer taught me some new games. I learned that when someone comes to the door, I must NOT jump on them. This was disappointing. Didn't he know how excited I was to see new people? But I guess I understand the rule: -- no jumping on visitors. When we finished lesson, I was tired. I lay down in the kitchen.

Mom and Dad listened to the trainer. He gave them some lessons to practice so I would have good manners. It would take time. The trainer said I am very smart, almost too smart. (And I AM a cute dog!) He told them to spend time with me because I am a problem solver. He told them I would solve problems they didn't even know they have! Then he laughed. Why did he laugh? I am a very smart dog!

He also told them I need lots of exercise, like long walks to use all my energy. He said I need a job, so I feel part of the family. My trainer said when Mom and Dad take me for a walk, I should have a dog backpack to carry. This will help me feel like I am helping.

My trainer told them a smart dog like me gets bored easily, so I need a special puzzle to use my brain. I like fun puzzles where I have to find treats. I love treats! He told Mom and Dad to play music when they left the house so I would feel comfortable when they are not at home. When they left, they told me they would be back. That made me feel loved and safe. Mom bought me a puzzle to keep me busy because I am so smart. I

Pet care
& Training

Sumo

Cat   Dog

29

loved it! We got to play with the puzzle every morning before breakfast to get my day off to a good start.

My trainer said I should go to a dog park to learn to get along with other dogs besides just Miso. I would get to be a big dog, and it is very important to be friendly and not bully other dogs. Close to our house was a special place for dogs, and every Saturday afternoon they had a play time for puppies. People could come too.

I loved play time! I was with other puppies. I was excited to be with dogs my own age, but I was twice as big as the other puppies! I would run to play with other puppies, but the smaller puppies got scared! They were afraid of me! They said I was a big bully! I didn't mean to scare them! That made me sad.

Then the dog park people moved me to the big dog area, even though I was just a puppy! I was a little smaller than the big dogs, but I was not afraid. I was excited to meet more dogs! I would run fast, roll over, jump, and look straight at each dog. But I was still scaring the other dogs and their people! Dad and Mom decided to wait to let me learn more manners at home from my sister, Miso. So, home we went.

Dad and Mom and did the driveway lessons with me every day for months until I learned the rules. We took long walks twice a day, and they talked to me. Some days we ran. I was learning manners for city life.

Sumo Practices Doga

My trainer also suggested a doggie yoga class. Mom decided to find a new thing for me called Doga. I thought, what is yoga? What is doga? I learned that yoga is a calming exercise. Doga is dog yoga. Mom loves yoga. Mom loves me, so she thought I would like doga too. It would be something we could both share.

There was a special class in Houston, so Mom signed us up for Monday night. Mom and I drove to class. You know I love car rides, so I got to look out the window at all the new sights. I had never traveled in that direction before. At first, there were bayous of water, people walking on trails, people on bicycles, and people running on paths. It was pretty. Then the scenery changed. There were lots of cars, narrow streets with construction, and lots of office buildings and skyscrapers. Mom said it was "downtown." Finally, Mom and I arrived at the doga place.

Mom checked us in at the counter. We waited until the teacher took us to the doga room. (This teacher was called a trainer, too.) The room was big with a hard floor. There were a lot of dogs and people waiting for class to begin. The owners were standing around the room quietly. Dogs were meeting other dogs, sniffing and walking around them to get to know them before class started. I thought I was going to like this class.

The trainer came into the class and told us it was going to be fun! The first night started with a warmup -- just walking on a leash with Mom. I knew what to do already, but I really had to pay attention. When Mom said "sit" she wanted me to sit – fast! I had to walk beside her when Mom asked me to "heel." Sometimes Mom had to use a clicker to get my attention, and it did. I wanted to do a good job and please Mom.

Sometimes the trainer had us walk in circles. Sometimes we walked in figure eights. Mom and I were in a room with seven other dogs and seven owners and two trainers. All the dogs had to behave and pay attention to their owners. Once the warmup routine was completed, then the doga lessons started.

The trainer explained doga is a special way for people to work with their dog, and it is fun! He said it gives dogs emotional stimulation, calms the mind, relaxes, and gives better flexibility. What does all that mean? I just knew I like to please Mom and it was fun. I am a good, smart dog.

Mom helped me with special poses. Pose one was "chaturanga." The teacher said it is a resting pose. Mom had me lie on my tummy with my front paws extended. Mom patted my back. This pose is a very relaxing pose and was a good way to get started.

The next pose was "chair pose." Mom knelt behind me and lifted my front paws out. I was standing on my back legs. My front paws were extended like the arms of a chair. Did you ever try yoga? Do they teach it at your school?

The next pose was "heart to heart." Because I was a bigger puppy than the rest of the dogs, Mom knelt behind me and lifted me up. She put one hand on my heart and held me close. I could feel her chest since it was pressed into my back. I could hear her breathing and felt her hand on my heart. This was my favorite pose. I love my Mom!

The last pose was called "sa-vas-ana." People do this too, but it is different for dogs.

I lay on a yoga mat on my back with my belly faced toward the ceiling. My paws were pointed to the corners of the mat. Mom patted me and rubbed my belly. I liked this pose also.

After this final pose, my trainer told us to practice every day until class next week. Next week, we would all do this and then learn some new poses.

When Mom put me in the front seat of the car, I lay across the seat with my head on her lap. I fell asleep fast. (Mom says I snore!) I slept the whole way home. Mom had to wake me when we got home. I was so relaxed that I followed Mom into the house and lay down and slept the whole night -- and so did Mom! It was a great night. I love my Mom!

Sumo Goes for Rides

Ijust love to go for rides! When I hear the keys rattle, I know someone is going out – maybe me! My family sometimes takes me for a ride in the big green truck. Sometimes we go in the car. Dad and Mom let me sit in the back seat, and I wear a special seat belt. They roll down the back window a little bit so I can feel the wind on my face as we drive. They play music, too, which makes the trip even more fun.

I would like to go for a ride with them every day, but they must work. We do the most fun things on Saturday and Sunday. One Saturday I heard Mom and Dad talking about going out and getting coffee. I thought it was weird because I see them drink coffee at home. I was very quiet until they got the keys and said I was going to go in the truck for a ride! I was jumping up and down and so excited that they couldn't get my leash on me! Finally, I settled down so they could put on my leash, and we got to go in the truck.

They rolled down the window, and I could feel the wind in my face. The music was playing. We had only gone a short way when they drove into a coffee place called "Starbucks." We waited in line in the truck. They ordered coffee. We pulled up to the window so Dad could pay. Then the biggest surprise ever happened…. guess what? The coffee lady saw me. (They call coffee ladies "baristas.") She thought I was so cute and handsome. (She was right, of course!) Then she asked Dad if I could have a special treat, and he said "Yes!" I wondered what it could be?

The lady gave Dad a special cup. Dad gave the cup to Mom. Mom let me lick from the cup. It was not coffee. It was the most delicious thing I had ever tasted! Better than yogurt! It was sweet and creamy. They call it "whipped cream." I licked the cup clean. Wow! I did not think a ride could get any better until now. Thank you, Starbucks! I wanted to come back again and again. Every morning I went to the back door hoping we could get in the truck and get more of that whipped cream in a cup.

Sumo Loves the Backyard

I had been living with my forever family in Houston for about five years. I spent more and more time outside. I loved my fenced yard that went from the front to the back behind the garage. I could run all day back and forth. I also loved sitting on the big rock (they called it a "boulder") in the front yard and being King of the Neighborhood. I thought I looked pretty cool and in charge.

For a while, pretty much every night was the same: dinner, walk, brush teeth, and then off to bed. One special morning I woke Mom to go potty outside – she said it was 4 o'clock. Is that too early? Dad was sound asleep. Mom opened the back door and let me out. She sat in the kitchen waiting for me to come and scratch on the back door to come back in.

I wondered what was taking Sumo so long outside? I went to the back door and called his name. Sumo did not come. That was really strange. I walked outside and could not see Sumo anywhere -- now I was really getting worried! I ran upstairs to get a flashlight to help me see in the dark. I went to the back of the yard where it was the darkest. It was hard to see Sumo in the dark because of his black fur. All of a sudden, I heard a noise, and it scared me! What was it? I moved the flashlight to shine where I heard the noise.

I know I looked funny. My head was stuck under the fence and my butt and tail were up in the air. Very embarrassing! Mom called me but I could not move. I knew I would probably get into trouble because I did not come when called. Another rule of the house.

Finally, Mom pulled me away from the fence. She was surprised when she put the light on me. I had a possum in my mouth! Mom screamed! She made me drop it even though I did not want to! We both ran back to the house with our hearts racing!

I went running up the stairs, screaming about what happened. I woke Dad up. He asked, "What is wrong?" I told him the story and warned him, "Don't kiss Sumo right now. He had a possum in his mouth."

My heart was still racing, but I went outside again to check the fence and see if the possum was dead. Nope! The possum had just played dead, and then it ran off. I saw there was a big hole at the bottom of the fence.

I knew Sumo would come straight back there and find the hole again, and the next time he might actually go under the fence, because he is so smart and a problem solver and would find a way to the next yard. I did not want that to happen. I ran back upstairs and asked Dad to put something in front of the hole until we could fix it right.

Dad did not have any boards. It was dark, and Dad was still very sleepy. However, he is very smart (like me), and he took our ironing board and propped it up against the hole. They said that would do temporarily. (What is "temporarily"?) Mom said I smelled like possum which grossed her out. She brushed my teeth. What an exciting morning! (She was right; I would have found that hole. But wish I could have kept the possum!)

Sumo Goes to the Groomer

After our possum adventure, Mom and Dad said I needed a bath, so I was going to a groomer. I was not really sure what that meant, but we got into the truck and rode to a store.

There were lots of dogs waiting there. The lady took me back to the bath area. She was called a "groomer." First there was warm water and soap. I had soap bubbles all over me, but she was very careful not to get soap into my eyes. She rubbed the soap into my fur. It felt good. The groomer rinsed the soap off, then she blew warm air into my fur with a hair dryer. That was a bit weird. It was loud. It took forever because I have a lot of fur.

Once she started drying my fur, it began to fly all over the place! There was black and white fur in the air, on the table, on the floor, on the windows and doors. The groomer was covered in my fur. It looked like a fur tornado! Finally, my fur was dry.

The groomer put some good smelling stuff all over me. Then she clipped my toenails, and I was ready to go. (Some of the girl dogs got nail polish, but I am a boy dog. Not for me!) Finally, she gave me a bright green kerchief for my neck.

The groomer called Dad and Mom to pick me up. When Mom and Dad saw me, they looked so happy. I know it was because I looked so good and smelled so good! We went outside for a short walk and then back in the truck to go home. I was very thirsty from my big day and got a huge drink of water. Then I took a three-hour nap. It was an exciting day. I thought one day I would want to go back -- but not too soon. Would they give me another cool kerchief? Maybe a red one next time.

47

Sometimes Parents Need a Vacation

My life in Houston was great, and then I learned that Mom and Dad were going on vacation. Surely Miso and I would be going with them, right? The next thing that happened was we found out they hired a pet sitter, a lady named Trish. Trish came to visit the house to get to know me and Miso. She was friendly and knew a lot about dogs. Miso and I thought she might be a little strict. But we trusted Mom and Dad to keep us safe, and yet I still wanted to go with them.

Then Mom and Dad were getting ready, packing, and getting tickets to go on vacation. They told Miso and me we were not going on this trip. But I had a job. I was in charge of guarding the house and taking care of

Miso. I am a big brave dog, and Mom and Dad expected me to look after my sister even though she is older than me. I think Miso liked that part because she does not like to be in charge.

Mom told us Trish would come to the house four times a day. Mom left a long list of things we like and important information: our treats, our food, our routine, our vet's phone number, and such. Mom and Dad love us and want us to be safe. Dad and Mom left with their bags. They said they would be back in three days. I was a little sad and a little scared, but I tried to understand and be brave. Trish was really nice, and we had fun.

Soon three days passed, and Miso and I were at the back door to greet Mom and Dad. We were so excited to see them! I had watched the house and protected Miso. Trish did a good job. Mom and Dad gave Miso and me a hug and kiss and told us how much they missed us. Everything seemed OK. Mom and Dad took their luggage upstairs. Then they left the house again – without us! They got in the car – without us! They said they were going out to dinner. Bummer!

I thought, "I am so mad! How can you leave me again when you just got home?" I ran straight upstairs and into the bedroom. I went to Dad's side of the bed and pulled his favorite pillow off the bed. It was soft, and when I shook it and played with it, I discovered it had thousands

of goose down feathers inside! I bit and growled and shook that pillow! I destroyed it! There were feathers everywhere. Feathers were on the bed, the floor, the ceiling fan, draperies, furniture -- all the way down the stairs. It was so much fun! I could have fun without Dad and Mom!

Miso did not have fun with me. She was totally freaked out and went into hiding. She knew when Mom and Dad got home, they would be upset. Miso knew she would get into trouble, and she did not want that. Miso has sensitive feelings and knows how to follow the rules.

We returned to the house within an hour. We walked through the back door and into the house, but something was wrong. No dogs came to greet us. It was very quiet. I looked everywhere. No dogs, and it was very, very quiet.

I immediately went upstairs and saw something white. What was it? Feathers? Where did the feathers come from? Then I saw the whole bedroom covered in feathers! There Sumo was, sitting next to the bed, so proud and happy for what he had done. Miso was hiding in the bathroom because she knew she would get into trouble. I yelled for Dad. He came running. We just stood there and stared at all the feathers – and at Sumo.

Mom found Miso and patted her. They could tell she was scared. They ignored me. They said they would "deal with me later when they were not mad." They cleaned up the mess. It took them a long time – actually three days!

So -- Mom and Dad learned it was not a good idea to come home after vacation and leave again for dinner. I was definitely mad and hurt. But I learned it was not OK to play with Dad's favorite pillow and the feathers. There were consequences. No treats for three days.

You know what? I have heard them telling this story to their friends, and LAUGHING! They didn't know you could have a feather snowstorm inside your house! I showed them how! They will remember it forever! (And it was fun!)

Sumo Goes to the Country

Dad and Mom took me to the country for the weekend. They had a weekend house, and one day we would live there permanently. We drove a long way in the truck. As soon as I got out, the country reminded me of Kentucky, where I was born. Everywhere I looked was grass and trees. It was exciting with so many new smells in the air. Mom kept me on a leash so I would not get lost. We went for a long walk. I saw rabbits, deer, armadillos, and birds. There were no city sounds like traffic or sirens going by. It was quiet. The air was crisp. I loved it. I did not want the walk to end. When we got to the house, I was so thirsty and tired. I had a big drink of water and then lay down to nap. When I woke up, I could not wait to go outside again and explore.

I found a place to nap on a cool wood floor at the front door. I could see out of the glass door and the windows on each side. I did not even have to get up to see what was going on outside. I just looked up to see everything.

For the next year we visited the country every weekend. I learned about seasons. The Spring is bright and sunny. Flowers, plants, and grass grow everywhere. There are new smells in the air. Dad said we must be careful on our walks because snakes come out of hibernation. I did not know what that meant. (What is "hibernation?") But one day, I found out. We were on our morning walk and Dad carried a big stick with him. What was the stick for? We walked along and I was smelling everything. Suddenly, a big rattlesnake came out of the woods! I saw it first, then Dad saw it. He was so quick. He used the stick to get the snake off the path so we could walk safely.

Then I understood what Dad meant. In Winter, snakes go deep in the woods to stay warm. In Spring when the weather warms up, snakes come out of the deep woods, so you really must be careful. I felt safe with my Dad by my side with the big stick.

Next is Summertime. It is really hot in Texas. Sometimes it is 100 degrees! I really like being in our yard to play, but I spend very little time outside when it is so hot. I just go out for a quick walk in the morning and the evening. The sun beats down on my black fur and skin and it is too much. It makes me pant, and I drink lots of water!

The next season is Fall, and I think it is my favorite. The weather gets cooler and there is a nice afternoon breeze. We spend most afternoons on the porch that goes around the house. We get to watch the birds drink from the lake outside the house. We get to see the fish in the lake. The deer come closer and closer to the house. Dad is very relaxed when we are in the country. He started feeding the fish in the lake in the afternoons. I liked seeing them come to the top of the water and eat their snacks. This is a safe place for all animals, birds, and fish to live peacefully together.

Finally, Winter comes, and the temperature is much colder. I like staying outside more and more. The wind gets cold, and I sometimes stay outside in the back yard for hours. Dad is not worried about me staying in the back yard because he knows how much I love it, and usually I cannot get into trouble until....

One night I was looking around the garden and saw an animal move. I ran to check it out and surprised an animal I had not seen before. Ha! The surprise was on me -- it was a skunk! I had never seen a skunk before. It was black and white, like me. But my surprise turned into the skunk's surprise, and the skunk turned around, flipped its tail, and sprayed me. Ugh! Whatever it was, I smelled terrible. When I got to the back door, Dad knew something was wrong.

Oh my gosh did Sumo ever stink! He had been sprayed by a skunk. There was no way he could come into the house smelling like that. I had to get a bucket and prepare a special bath. I just wanted to stay in bed and drink my coffee in peace, but I love Sumo and he needed me. I got the baking soda, hydrogen peroxide, liquid detergent, and water to get ready. I gave Sumo a bath so he could come back into the house. It was early morning. I waited until 7:00 and then called the groomer and made an appointment to bring stinky Sumo in immediately for a bath!

Dad put me in the truck and off we went. Time for another bath and cologne treatment! I will not ever make that mistake again! Another rule: Avoid skunks! Pew-eeee!

Sumo Goes to the Farmers' Market

One beautiful Spring Saturday morning and Dad and I went to the Farmer's Market. We got into the big green truck and rode down a country road. I had never been to a farmers' market, so this would be a new adventure. Dad parked and got out of the truck. He said, "Let's go!" I jumped out and we walked to the market.

I was on my leash. There were tables with all kinds of things. The first table had lots of jellies and jams. There was strawberry, blueberry, cherry, apple butter, and may haw jelly. Each type was in a special glass jar with a different colored top.

The next table sold all different kinds of honey. Then a table with just pecans. Then a table with beef jerky. Then a table with things made of yarn. The next area had cool yard art. I carefully walked around the

BAKERY

SALE

Organic Farm

59

yard art so I would not break anything. Another rule! Some of the stuff was bigger than me! There were metal chickens, roosters, bulls, windmills, and things all painted in bright colors. Funny!

Next, we walked into the center of the Farmers' Market. Everything was in wooden boxes. There were tomatoes, cucumbers, potatoes, corn, onions, radishes, carrots, and lettuce. Then the next section had strawberries, blueberries, apples, lemons, limes, oranges, grapefruit, and watermelon. (This is stuff I usually don't eat. But Mom and Dad like it.)

Then two Girl Scouts in green uniforms came up and asked Dad about me. "What is his name?" Dad told them my name. They asked more questions. "Is he a dog? Is he a bear? How old is he? Is he a boy dog? What kind of dog is he? Where does he live?" Dad answered all their questions. He told them I am an Akita, a Japanese dog which is bred to hunt and protect the family. He told them I was eight, and where we live. The girls said I was beautiful. (They were smart girls, and very friendly. I AM a handsome dog!)

The girls were selling Girl Scout cookies. They asked Dad if he wanted to buy some. He said he would stop by their table when we headed back to the truck. I loved the attention from the two girls because they were petting me as they asked Dad all the questions.

The girls ran back screaming to their friends and their moms. They were yelling, "We met Sumo and he is eight and he is an Akita and he is a Japanese dog."

A few minutes later Dad and I walked to the Girl Scout cookie table. Then the other 13 Girl Scouts saw me and came running. Dad braced himself and me.

Oh my gosh! I had no idea what would happen. Was Sumo scared because so many girls were running toward him? Would he get freak out and bite them? I held on tight to the leash to protect Sumo and the girls. They didn't know it is a bad idea to race toward a dog, especially a big dog like Sumo. Then we were surrounded by the Girl Scout pack. They were petting and kissing him all over. I tried to keep Sumo calm, because I had no idea what was going to happen. I told the girls it is best to wait for instructions from the dog owner to learn how to best get to know a dog. I tried to get the Girl Scout moms' attention, but they were busy talking to each other and were not watching the girls.

Finally, I got the girls to be quiet and pay attention and to slowly get acquainted with Sumo. I explained to the girls they could pet him gently and could even kiss him! I explained they should not put their face near his mouth or pull his tail or grab his neck. I told the girls that Sumo was happy to meet them, and Sumo knew they were excited, but we all must follow these rules.

I just stood there! I have never seen so many girls all in one place and all wearing green Girl Scout dresses! Slowly Dad and I walked to the cookie table with all 13 girls in tow. Dad paid for two boxes of Girl Scout cookies and we got in the truck. We drove home. We were both very tired after such an exciting morning! I was very popular!

Sumo Moves to the Country

About six years after living in Houston, Dad, Miso, and I moved to the country. Mom stayed in the city to get the house ready to sell. Mom and Dad said I would be happier in the country, and people would be coming to look at the house all the time. I would not like strangers in our house. Mom would visit on the weekends.

Dad made great special meals and took us on long walks. Dad loved to cook, and I was his biggest fan! Some mornings he made scrambled eggs and bacon or ham and cheese omelets to change it up. For some reason he decided I was bored with regular dog food. For lunch, he would often make his famous roasted chicken, and he shared his lunch with me and Miso. Some nights, he prepared a grilled steak or liver for me. Dad knew my homeland was Japan and I had a special love of fish. On super special occasions, he would give me ahi tuna and rice. Yummy!

We did not have much company, but when new people came to visit it was a treat for me. I am loved and protected, and I really love my family.

Dad decided to retire in the country, and that is where we all stayed. The strangest thing happened the next winter in Texas. It snowed! I loved walking outside on the cold grass, hearing the crunching sounds, and feeling the chill in the air. I loved being in the country -- it reminded me of my home in Kentucky and the weather where my grandparents and great-grandparents lived.

Sumo's Forever Family

When I was a puppy on the farm in Kentucky, I wished I would have a forever family where I would be safe and loved. I did not want to worry about where I was going to sleep or if I had enough to eat or if I would be hurt.

As you can tell from reading my story, I did find my forever home. It was better than even I could have imagined as a puppy. I realized I was special because I was CHOSEN. Most people do not get to choose their family members, but when you are adopted you are wanted. It is a very special feeling and one that I will always treasure. Over the years we learned how to work together as a family. Everyone has a job in a family. The job changes each year as you get older. In the early years my family protected me and taught me many things. Now that I am a big boy dog, I protect my family -- that is just the way it is!

Sumo Meets His New Neighbor

My story does not end here. Dad made friends years ago with the rancher next door, whose name is Chris. On our long walks we would see Chris on the tractor in his fields. Often times we would be walking down the fence line and Chris would stop and get off his tractor and come over and give a Texas greeting. This went on for years.

One day Chris was walking the fence line on his side, and we were walking on the other side. Dad stopped to say good morning to Chris. This time Chris had a small boy with him – that was odd! Chris was always in the field alone. Chris introduced Dad and Miso and me to the boy, Lucas. Dad smiled and said hello. Miso and I wagged our tails and our bums!

Later that day Chris called Dad to come over and help in the field. Dad always went to help his neighbor. When Dad got home, he told me

Lucas was Chris' son. I wondered what a "son" was. Chris did not have children.

Well, all that changed! Chris wanted a son in order to complete his family and share outdoor activities together. They really wanted to have a complete family. There was an empty space in their hearts that could only be filled with a little boy. They went through the very long process of adoption, and soon Lucas will have his forever family like me!

I cannot wait until we go on our walk tomorrow and I help Lucas understand about all the great things that are about to happen in his life! He has been chosen! He is special and loved and safe! We both have forever families! He will be my new best friend!

Afterward

We could have shared many other stories: celebrating birthday parties, going to the beach or the park or sitting in front of the fireplace and feeling the warmth with family close by, visiting family, Dad's cooking special meals, big family dinners, holidays, or just simple routines.

From reading this book, what we want you to experience is the unconditional love of family and what a great adoption can look like and become, whether you are a dog, like Sumo and Miso, or a boy or girl.

God knew all along the plan He had for Sumo, Miso, Mom, and Dad, and we are so grateful. Not every story ends this way with adoptive families, but we pray yours has a happy ending.

CPSIA information can be obtained
at www.ICGtesting.com
Printed in the USA
LVHW020405161020
668894LV00007B/263

9 781641 843706